CW00404928

Edward
ELGAR

The Music Makers
Op. 69

Vocal Score
Klavierauszug

SERENISSIMA MUSIC, INC.

ORCHESTRA

2 Flutes
Piccolo
2 Oboes
English Horn
2 Clarinets
Bass Clarinet
2 Bassoons
Contrabassoon

4 Horns
3 Trumpets
3 Trombones
Tuba

Timpani
2 Percussion
2 Harps
Organ

Violin I
Violin II
Viola
Violoncello
Bass

Duration: ca. 35 minutes

Premiere: October 1, 1912
Birmingham, England
Birmingham Triennial Music Festival
Alto Solo, Chorus and Orchestra / Composer

ISBN: 1-932419-58-6
This score is a slightly modified unabridged reprint of the
score published in 1912 by Novello & Co., Ltd.
The score has been enlarged to fit the present format.

Printed in the USA
First Printing: July, 2003

The Music Makers

Op. 69

3

Arthur O'Shaughnessy

Edward Elgar

SERENISSIMA MUSIC, INC.

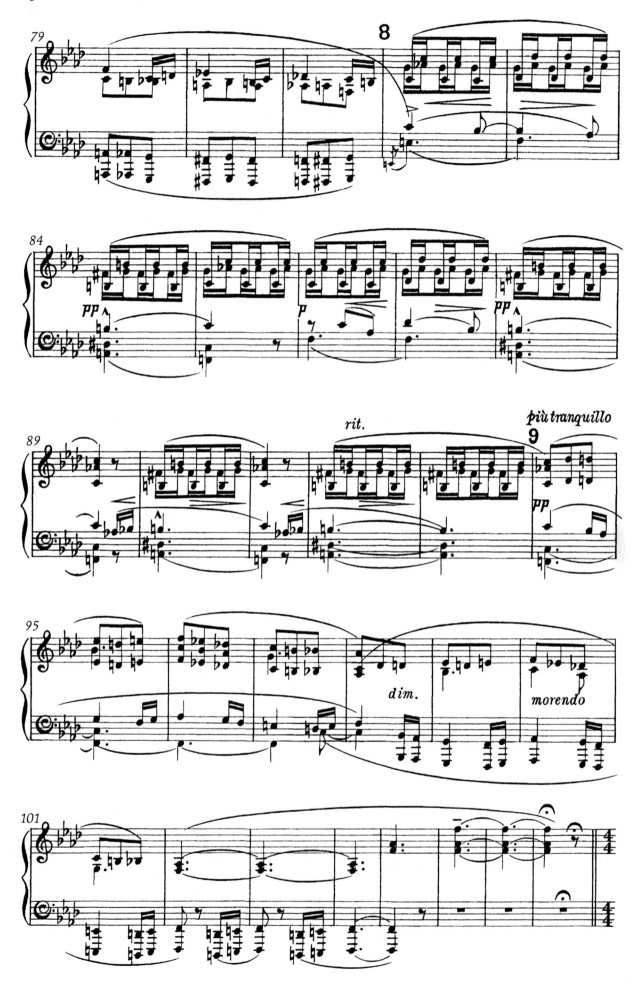

can trample a king-dom down.

down, can trample a king-dom down.

can trample a king-dom down.

can trample a king-dom down.

(Drums.)

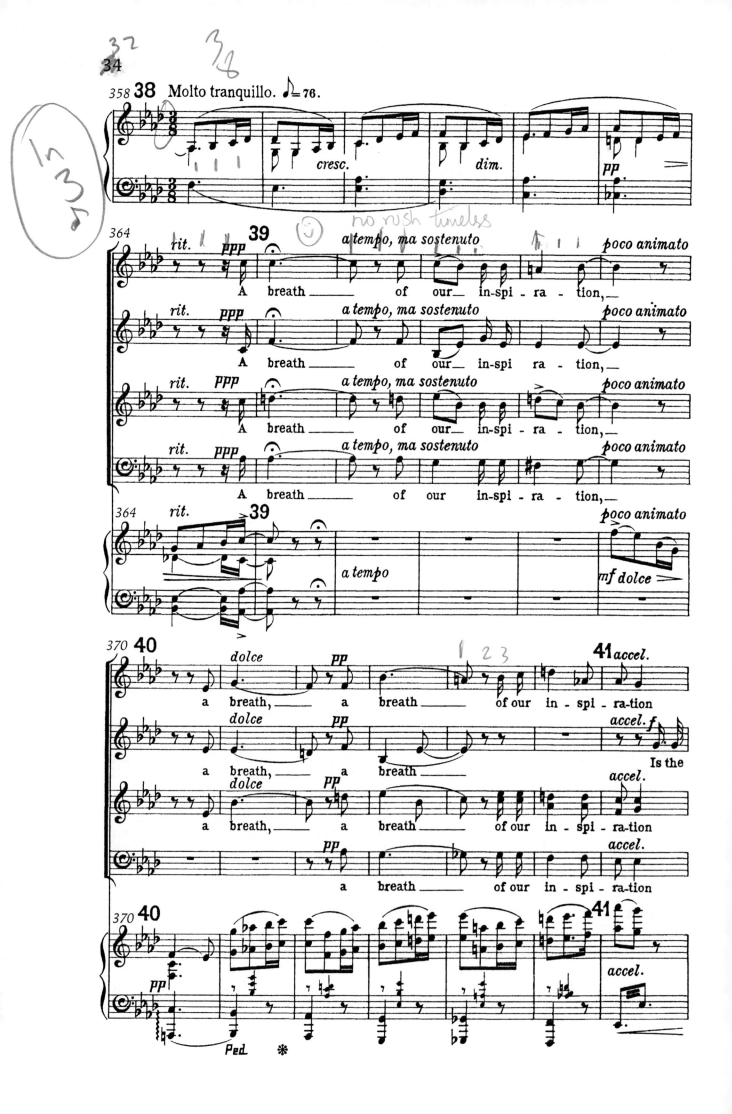

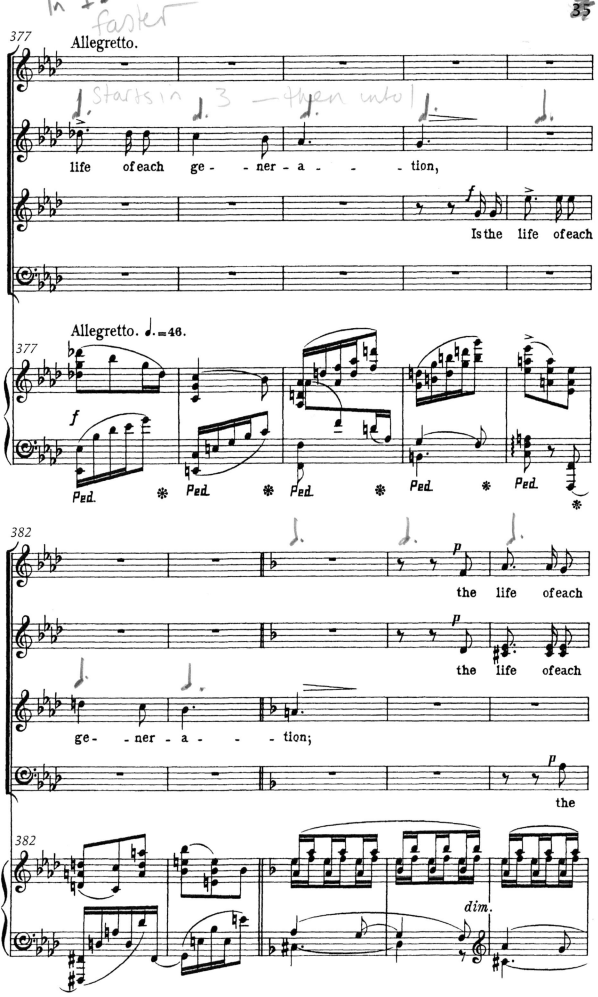

more expression

397 *poco a poco animato*

-pos-si-ble seem-ing,   a   wondr-   -ous thing, The

a   wondr-ous thing, a   wondr-   -ous thing, The

-pos-si-ble seem-ing,   a   wondr-   -ous thing, The

a   wondr-ous thing, a   wondr-   -ous thing, The

401 **44** Più allegro ma maestoso.

soldier,   the   king,___   and the pea-sant   Are work-ing___to-ge-ther in

soldier,   the   king,___   and the pea-sant   Are work-ing___to-ge-ther in

soldier,   the   king,___   and the pea-sant   Are work-ing___to-ge-ther in

soldier,   the   king,___   and the pea-sant   Are work-ing___to-ge-ther in

401 **44** Più allegro ma maestoso. ♩=108.

555

558 63

*Grt change tempo from ♪
to ♪. (urgent)*

82 Tempo primo.

nigh,

nigh,

nigh,

nigh,

82 Tempo primo. ♪=138.

ff con fuoco

And al - ready goes forth the warn-ing That

And al - ready goes forth the warn-ing That

And al - ready goes forth the warn-ing That

And al - ready goes forth the warn-ing That

f

fff

Yea, in spite of a dreamer, a dreamer who slumbers, And a sing-er who

sings no more,_____

No more._____

No more,_____

No more,_____

No more,_____

(Judge's Walk, N.W. 1912.)

Lightning Source UK Ltd.
Milton Keynes UK
UKOW012016081211

183428UK00009B/9/A